THE MEDIUM

tragedy in two acts

words and music by
gian carlo menotti

REVISED VERSION

vocal score
$4.00

g. schirmer, inc. / new york
[1967]

Note

All rights of any kind with respect to this opera and any part thereof, including but not limited to stage, radio, television, motion picture, mechanical reproduction, translation, printing, and selling, are strictly reserved.

License to perform this work, in whole or in part, must be secured in writing from the Publisher. Terms will be quoted upon request.

Copying of either separate parts or the whole of this work, by hand or by any other process, is unlawful and punishable under the provisions of the U. S. A. Copyright Act.

"The Medium" was conceived as a chamber opera for thirteen instruments and fourteen players: flute, oboe, clarinet, bassoon, horn, trumpet, percussion, piano (four hands), and string quintet. In larger theatres, a string orchestra may be employed in place of the quintet.

Orchestral materials and an arrangement of the orchestral score for two pianos are available on rental.

The use of any copies, including orchestrations, other than those issued by the Publisher, is forbidden.

All inquiries should be directed to the Publisher:

g. schirmer, inc.
609 FIFTH AVENUE
NEW YORK, N. Y. 10017

Characters

Monica,
     daughter of Madame Flora . . . . SOPRANO

Toby, *a mute*

Madame Flora *(Baba)* . . . . CONTRALTO

Mrs. Gobineau . . . . SOPRANO

Mr. Gobineau . . . . BARITONE

Mrs. Nolan . . . . MEZZO-SOPRANO

La scène se passe de nos jours dans le salon de Madame Flora. Une pièce sinistre, au mobilier démodé, dans un appartement des faubourgs d'une grande ville. Au fond de la scène côté cour, l'étroite cage d'un escalier intérieur descendant vers la porte d'entrée. Au fond de la scène côté jardin, un grand théâtre de marionnettes grossièrement construit, avec un rideau blanc au centre, suspendu à une tringle, pour cacher l'opérateur. A côté, un petit coffre. Sur le mur du fond, un grand graphique d'astrologie qui devient transparent quand on l'éclaire par l'arrière. Au premier plan, côté jardin, une porte. Au premier plan, côté cour, mais près du centre, une table à trois pieds d'aspect vieillot, au-dessus de laquelle pend un lustre rond de style Victorien qu'on allume au moyen d'une chaine. Dans un coin, une statuette de la Vierge, ornée d'un chapelet, et devant elle une petite veilleuse qui brûle dans un gobelet de verre rouge. Quatre chaises et un canapé. Sur le mur près de la cage de l'escalier, un bouton qui ouvre automatiquement la porte d'entrée. La sonnette de la porte doit avoir un son strident, de manière qu'on l'entende distinctement quelle que soit l'intensité de l'orchestre. Aucune fenêtre. L'heure de la journée à laquelle se déroule l'action sera toujours imprécise.

The action takes place in Madame Flora's parlor in our time. A squalid room in a flat on the outskirts of a great city. A narrow descending stairwell stage left (leading down to the street). Stage right at the rear a tall primitive puppet theater, with a white curtain to hide the standing puppeteer. Next to it a small trunk. On the back wall a large astrological chart which will become transparent when light is placed behind it. Downstage right a door. Upstage left, above the stairwell, a curtained doorway. Downstage left, near the center, an old-fashioned three-legged table. Suspended above it a circular lamp of the Victorian period, which is lighted by means of a string. In a corner a tiny statue of the Virgin, with a rosary hanging from it, and a small votive candle in front of it burning in a red glass jar. Four chairs and a couch. On the wall, near the top of the stairwell, a small buzzer which unlocks the door downstairs. The doorbell which announces the visitors below must be very loud and strident, so as to be clearly heard above the orchestra. No windows. The time of day will be ambiguous throughout the play.

The Medium

French version by
Léon Kochnitzky

ACT I

Words and Music by
Gian Carlo Menotti

41701 C

Lento ma non troppo ♪ = 88

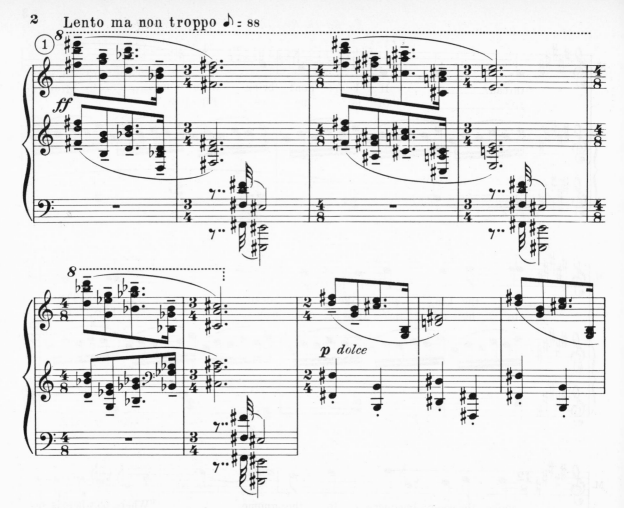

(As the curtain rises, Toby is seen kneeling near the open trunk from which he draws out brightly colored pieces of silk and bead necklaces, bangles, etc. With some of these he improvises for himself a fantastic costume. Monica stands near the couch, which is covered by a long white dress and a white veil. She holds a mirror in one hand, combing her loosened hair with the other)

(*Au lever du rideau, on voit Toby à genoux devant un coffre ouvert, Il en tire des morceaux de soie aux couleurs brillantes, des colliers de verroterie, des bracelets, etc. Il se compose un costume fantastique. Monica est debout près d'un divan recouvert d'une longue robe blanche et d'un voile blanc. Elle tient d'une main un petit miroir et de l'autre peigne ses cheveux défaits*)

Curtain up
Rideau

Andante calmo ♩ = 66

Monica

"Where, oh, where _____ is my new gold-en spin-dle and
«Où sont - ils _____ mon nou-veau fu-seau d'or et mon

(She suddenly sees Toby in her lifted
mirror and turns around)
(Dans son miroir levé, elle aperçoit
Toby et se retourne brusquement)

noth-ing, noth-ing is read-y! Be-sides, you know she'll beat you if you touch her things.
rien en-co-re n'est prêt! Et tu se-ras bat-tu, si tu touches à ses af-faires.

Tempo I

(She continues combing her hair)
(*Elle continue de se peigner*)

"Queen, fair queen,_____
"Bel - le rei -

___ if you give me the crown on your head,_____ I'll tell you
ne, don-ne-moi la cou-ronne à ton front_____ et ton fil

where I have seen_____ your gold - en spin-dle and
et ton fu - seau_____ bien - tôt te re - vien -

*All the recitatives throughout are to be sung very freely in regard to both rhythm and declamation.
*Tous les récitatifs doivent être chantés très librement, tant pour le rhythme que pour la déclamation.

8

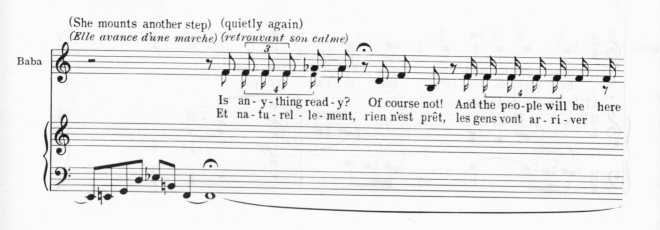

41701

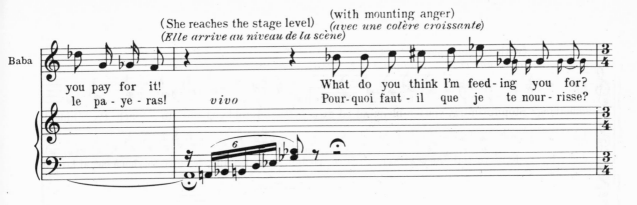

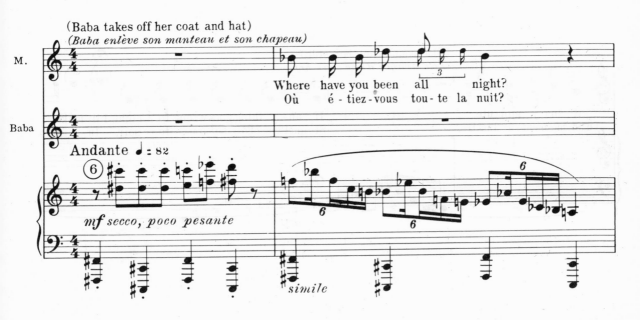

(throwing a roll of bills on the table)
(jetant sur la table un rouleau de billets)

Baba: Where have I been? Ah! ah! mon - ey, my dear, mon - ey! Look,
Où j'ai é - té? L'ar - gent, ma chère, l'ar - gent! Tiens,

M.: Where did you get it?
D'où vient cet ar - gent?

Baba: don't wor-ry, my sweet, you have a ver- y clev-er moth-er!
vois- tu, mon en-fant, ta mère est très in-tel - li - gen - te!

Where?
D'où?

Baba: I sat on Mrs. Cam- pi's steps all night; she
J'é - tais chez Ma - dame Bour - le - mont tout(e) la nuit; je

Allegro ♩=138 (Baba helps Monica into the white dress, and then
(*Baba aide Monica à endosser la robe blanche, puis*

Baba

Get read- y! Hur- ry!
Dé- pê-chez-vous, Al - lons!

covers her head with the white veil. In the meantime, Toby, after manipulating the lamp and the table, runs
elle lui couvre la tête d'un voile blanc. Pendant ce temps, Toby, après avoir manipulé la lampe et la table, tire

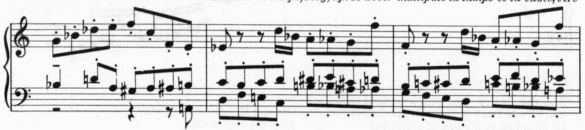

to the puppet theater, opens the curtain, revealing various levers and cables hidden behind it. He tests
le rideau du théâtre de marionnettes; on distingue alors un jeu compliqué de leviers et de câbles cachés der-

some of them, one of which levitates the table, another of which lowers the lamp)
*rière ce rideau; Toby vérifie les machines: celle qui fait tourner et se soulever la table, et celle qui fait
baisser la lampe)*

(The door-
bell rings)

(on entend
sonner à
la porte)

ppp

(At a signal from Baba,
Monica runs out from stage right. Toby hides
in the puppet theater, drawing the white
curtain in front of himself)
*(Monica sort en courant vers la droite de la
scène. Toby se cache dans le petit théâtre et
tire devant soi le rideau blanc)*

(Baba presses the buzzer which opens the latch-
(Baba presse le bouton qui ouvre la porte: puis

door downstairs, then gets a pack of cards
and sits in front of the table, pretending to
be absorbed in a game of solitaire)
*elle prend un paquet de cartes et s'assied
à la table; elle fait semblant de s'absorber
dans une patience)*

(Mr. and Mrs. Gobineau enter
from the stairwell)
*(Monsieur et Madame Gobineau,
arrivent au sommet de l'escalier)*

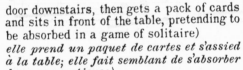

Mrs. Gobineau

Good evening, Madame Flo-ra.
Bon-soir, Ma-da-me Flo-ra.

Baba
(hardly looking up from her game)
(levant à peine les yeux de ses cartes)

Come in, come in.
En-trez, en-trez.

Mr. Gobineau

Good evening.
Bon - soir.

(senza misura)

41701

ner - vous. It is all ver - y sim - ple.
da - me. Tout ce - la est fort sim - ple.

p dolce

poco rall.

(A long pause, during which Baba gets up abruptly and exits. When Mrs. Nolan is quite sure that Baba has closed the door behind her, she leans confidentially toward Mr. Gobineau.)

(Un silence. Baba se lève brusquement et sort. Après s'être assurée que Baba a fermé la porte derrière elle, Madame Nolan se penche d'un air confidentiel vers Madame Gobineau.)

Have you known her a long time?

Vous la con-nais-sez de-puis long-temps?

(senza misura)

We
Nous ve -

Oh, yes! We have been com-ing here ev-'ry week for al-most two years.

Oh, oui! Nous ve-nons i-ci tou(tes) les se-maines de-puis près de deux ans.

Allegro molto ♩.= 88

(Mrs. Nolan, almost hysterical, springs up from her chair,
(Mme. Nolan dans un état d'agitation presque hystérique,

Baba: time to be-gin. Close the door.
lons com-men-cer. Fer-mez la porte.

ff agitato

dropping her pocketbook. Mrs. Gobineau picks it up for her, then helps her to take off her coat and
se lève brusquement; elle laisse tomber son sac. Mme. Gobineau ramasse le sac, aide Mme. Nolan à en-

leads her to the table. Meanwhile, Mr. Gobineau locks all the doors and helps Baba to place the
lever son manteau et elle la conduit à la table, tandis que M. Gobineau met le verrou aux portes et

⑯ **Molto meno mosso, quasi andante** ♩.= 76

f secco e pesante

chairs around the table.)
aide Baba à disposer les chaises autour de la table.)

(They all sit down, Baba facing the audience. Mrs. Gobineau shows Mrs. Nolan how to join hands around the table.)
*(Tous prennent place, Baba faisant face au public;
Mme. Gobineau montre à Mme. Nolan comment il faut
joindre les mains autour de la table.)*

(With a last look about her to see that everything is in order, Baba slowly and deliberately pulls the chain of the overhead lamp. The lights go out except the little candle in front of the Madonna.)

(Baba jette un dernier coup d'oeil autour d'elle pour s'assurer que tout est en ordre; puis, d'un geste lent et ferme, elle éteint la lampe au-dessus de la table. Les lumières s'éteignent, à l'exception de la veilleuse devant la statuette de la Vierge.)

(There is a long pause. Noticing Mrs. Nolan's nervousness, Mr. Gobineau leans towards her and speaks sotto voce.)

(Un silence. M. Gobineau s'aperçoit de la nervosité de Mme. Nolan; il se penche vers elle et lui parle à voix basse.)

(an even longer silence)

(un silence encore plus long)

Mr. Gobineau (freely)
(librement)

Mr. G.

You must be ver-y si-lent.   The hands   must touch.

Il faut sur-tout se taire.   Les mains doi-vent se touch-er.

pp sonoro (senza misura)

(Baba begins to moan, simulating a trance.)
(Baba, simulant une transe, se met à gémir.)

⑰ **Adagio** ♩ = 56

(very long)
(très long)

p espr.   *mf*   *ppp*

(Baba moans louder and louder.)
(Baba gémit de plus en plus fort.)

pp incalzando un po

(long)
(Baba suddenly breaks into a long, anguished scream.)
(Soudain, Baba éclate en un long cri d'angoisse.)

pp subito, ma sempre affannoso

ppp

(Behind the chart hanging on the wall, Monica slowly appears in a faint blue light. As Monica's voice is heard, Baba's moan dies away.)
(En transparence à travers le graphique suspendu au mur, Monica apparait lentement dans une faible lumière bleuâtre. Au son de la voix de Monica, le gémissement de Baba meurt dans sa gorge.)

Adagio ma non troppo ♩.= 50

Monica

M.

pp

Moth - er, moth - er,   are you there?   Moth - er, moth - er,   are you there?
Mè - re, mè - re,   est - ce toi?   Mè - re, mè - re,   est - ce toi?

(18)

pp sempre

M.

Moth - er, moth - er,   are you there?   Moth - er, moth - er,   are you there?
Mè - re, mè - re,   est - ce toi?   Mè - re, mè - re,   est - ce toi?

Mrs. Nolan

Mrs. N.

Oh!   oh!
Oh!   oh!

Mr. Gobineau *(agité)* (excitedly)

Mr. G.

Mis - sis No - lan,   it must be your   daugh - ter...   Speak to her!
Madame No - lan,   vo - tre fil - le sans   doute...   Par - lez lui!

Andante, senza trascinare ♩=54
(with great tenderness)
p (très tendrement)

Mum - my, Mum-my dear, you must not cry for me.
O __ Ma-man ché - rie, ne pleu - re pas pour moi.

p dolce

I'm still with you. What is death but a sweet-er change,
Je suis tout près. La mort n'est qu'un é - tat meil-leur,

poco movendo   *poco rit.*

there's no part-ing, there's no end. Mum - my, Mum-my
il n'y a ni a - dieu ni fin. O __ Ma-man ché -

poco rit.   *a tempo*   *a tempo*

dear, your sor-row's like a wound __ that keeps me a-
rie, tes pleurs me font souf-frir, __ et je reste é - veil-

mf   *p*

41301

Poco meno   *poco rit.* Tempo Iº

and prom-ise me nev-er to cry a-gain.   Mum - my, Mum-my
et promets-moi de ne ja-mais pleu rer.   O____ mè-re ché-

dear, oh, let me sleep in peace, my night is long. For-
rie, lais(se) moi dor-mir en paix, ma nuit est longue. Ou-

get,_____ for-get my grave, let the si-lent grass
blie,_____ ou-blie ma tombe, et qu'un vert ga-zon

clothe my bones.   Burn all my shoes, give a-way my brace-lets.
cou-vre mes os.   Brû-le mes sou-liers, donne au-si mes ba-gues.

M. Burn, burn, give a-way, give a-way. Keep for your-self on - ly the lit-tle
Brûle, brûle, don-ne tout, don-ne tout. Ne gar-de pour toi que le pe-tit mé-dail-

M. gold lock-et.
lon doré.

Mrs. Nolan (bewildered)
(très surprise)

Mrs. N. The gold lock-et? Which lock-et? I have no lock-et.
Le mé-dail-lon? Quel mé-dail-lon? Je n'en ai pas.

(senza misura)

(begins to disappear little by little)
(disparaissant peu à peu)

M. Moth - er, moth-er, are you there? Moth - er, moth-er, are you there?
Mè - re, mè - re, est-ce toi? Mè - re, mè - re, est-ce toi?

Mrs. N. I don't un-der - stand... Dood-ly, Dood-ly, don't go a -
Je ne com-prends pas... Chou-te, Chou-te, ne t'en vas

(come prima)

pp

34

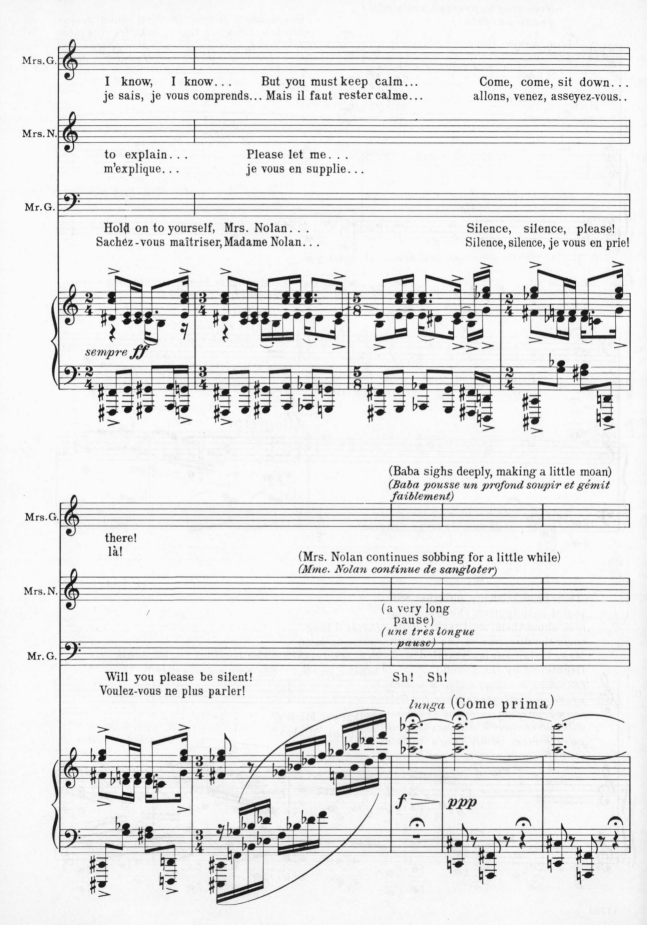

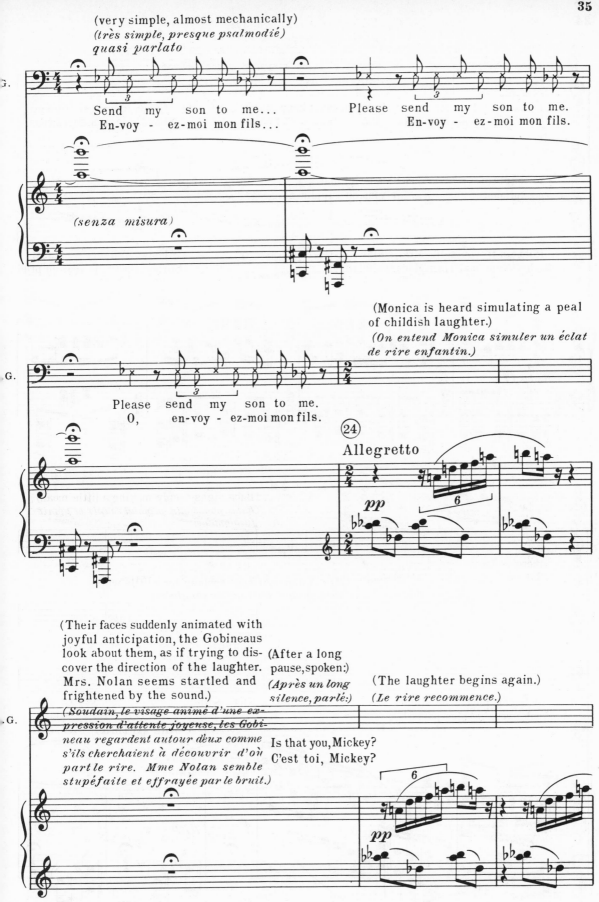

(Smiling, her eyes closed, Mrs.
Gobineau lifts her face as if
to receive the kisses of her
ghostly child.)
*(Souriant, les yeux clos, Mme. Go-
bineau lève la tête comme pour
recevoir les baisers de son enfant
fantôme.)*

sweet, kiss me.
chéri, embrasse-moi.

We'll be back soon.
Nous reviendrons bientôt.

(complete silence)
(silence complet)

(There is a long pause. Suddenly, with a loud gasp,
Baba clutches at her throat
with both hands.)
*(Un long silence. Brusque-
ment, Baba étouffe un cri
strident et porte vivement
les mains à sa gorge.)*

Baba

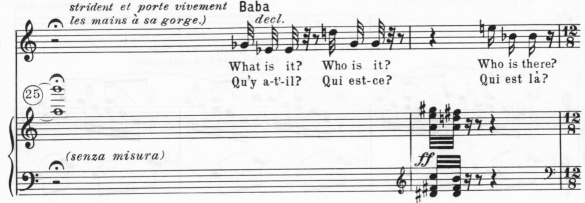

What is it? Who is it? Who is there?
Qu'y a-t'-il? Qui est-ce? Qui est là?

(senza misura)

(Baba gets up suddenly, throwing her chair back and turns on the light. She looks terror-
(Baba se lève tout à coup, repousse sa chaise et rallume la lumière. Terrifiée, elle

stricken at her clients, then runs wildly to the top of the stairwell and looks down, then runs back. The
examine ses visiteurs, puis elle court, très agitée, à la rampe d'escalier et regarde vers le bas, elle

clients looks at each other in great amazement and whisper among themselves)
revient vers la table. Les visiteurs se regardent les uns les autres, stupéfaits, et se parlent à voix basse)

42

Baba: there... I felt on my skin... ev-'ry fin-ger... see... like this!
vé... et j'ai sen-ti cha-que doigt sur ma peau...tiens... comm' ça!

subito poco accel.

Baba: Mon-i-ca, Mon-i-ca, I'm a-fraid! Yes, I'm a-fraid!
Mo-ni-ca, Mo-ni-ca, j'ai très peur! Oui, j'ai très peur!

poco rit. **ff**

(She draws the curtain of the puppet
theatre, revealing Toby, motionless,
as if in a trance.)
*(Elle tire le rideau du petit théâtre, on
découvre Toby, immobile, comme en
état d'hypnose.)*

Allegro molto ♩ = 112

(Toby starts)
(Toby sursaute)

Baba: Where is To-by? He! He's the one! I
Où est To-by? Lui! C'est donc lui! J'ai

㉚

ff **ff** **ff**

Just be-cause he can-not speak   we take him for a half -
Par - ce qu'il ne par - le pas   tu crois qu'il est si simple —

wit,   but he knows a great   deal. He knows   much
—   Et pour-tant il en sait   long, il sait   bien

more than we think.   There is some-thing un-can-ny a - bout him.   He
plus qu'on ne croit,   il a quel - que chose de trouble.   Il

sees   things   we don't see.   Get up!   Get
voit   des choses in - vi - si - bles.   De - bout!   De -

(Monica draws her away from Toby. She sits down, and Baba lies at her feet, her head on Monica's lap)
(Monica l'entraîne loin de Toby. Elle s'assied et Baba s'étend à ses pieds, appuyant la tête sur les genoux de sa fille)

Come, Ba-ba.
Voy-ons, Ba-ba.

Come, Ba-ba.
Voy-ons, Ba-ba.

(Monica begins gently to rock Baba)
(Monica commence à la bercer doucement)

Allegretto, con moto ♩ = 74

The sun has fall - en and it
Il est tom - bé le so -

(Toby, already oblivious of what has happened, takes an old tambourine from under the couch, and lying on the floor, accompanies the tune with soft taps on the instrument)
(Toby, ayant déjà oublié ce qui vient de se passer, prend sous le divan un vieux tambourin, et couché par terre, le frappe doucement en cadence pour accompagner la berceuse)

lies in blood. The moon is weav - ing band - a - ges of gold.
leil san - glant, la lu - ne tis - se des pan - se - ments d'or.

ritenuto *a tempo*

M. O black swan, where, oh, where has my lov-er gone?
Cy - gne noir, dis - moi, dis - moi, où est mon a - mi?

M. I had giv-en him a kiss of fire, And a gold-en ring,
Qu'il re - çoi - ve mon bai - ser de flammes, et mon an-neau d'or,

M. and a gold-en ring. Don't you hear your lov-er moan?
et mon an-neau d'or. En - tends - tu gé - mir ton a - mi?

poco più mosso

M. Eyes of glass and feet of stone, Shells for teeth and
Pieds de pierr(e), les yeux de glace, Dents de nacre et

*Mrs. Gobineau may sing this part off stage.

*Mme Gobineau peut chanter ce passage derrière le décor.

M.

The moon is weav-ing band-a-ges of gold.
La lu - ne tis - se des pan - se-ments d'or.

Baba
tecum etc. *Sancta Maria,*

③⑦ Allegretto con moto

ppp

M.

O black wave, O black wave, Take me down with you, take me down with you.
Fleu - ve noir, fleu - ve noir, Prends-moi sur tes ondes, prends-moi sur tes ondes.

Baba
Mater Dei etc.

(Baba suddenly stops praying. Child's laughter is heard as Baba hides her head in Monica's lap)
(Baba interrompt tout à coup sa prière. On entend un rire d'enfant; Baba se cache la tête sur les genoux de Monica)

M.

pp

(curtain)
(rideau)

ACT II

(Same setting as Act I – evening, a few days later)
(Même décor qu'au Ier acte – un soir, quelques jours plus tard)

①

(Monica is sitting in front of the puppet theater watching a performance)
(Assise devant le théâtre de marionnettes, Monica assiste au spectacle)

Allegro ♩. = 120

'The puppets have fallen in a heap.
Toby comes out to acknowledge
Monica's applause.)
*(Les marionnettes tombent l'une
sur l'autre. Toby se montre et
Monica l'applaudit.)*

Monica
(liberamente)

Bra - vo! And af - ter the the - a - ter, sup - per and dance. Mu - sic! Um - pa - pa, um - pa - pa,
Bra - vo! A - près le spec - tacle, _ sou - per et bal: Mu - si - que! Tra - la - la, tra - la - la,

Allegretto ♩.= 58

(During this song, Toby, barefooted, dances about the stage)
(Pendant que Monica chante, Toby, pieds-nus, parcourt la scène en dansant)

Up in the sky some - one is play - ing a trom - bone and a gui - tar.
② Là - haut, là - haut, la gui - tare et le trom - bo - ne font un du - o.

p (Allegretto ♩.= 58)

Red is your tie, and in your vel - ve - tine coat you hide a star.
Rouge est ton voile, _ et ca - ché dans ta man - tille _ brille une é - toile. _

poch. ritenuto

41701

Mon - i - ca, Mon - i - ca, dance the waltz,   Mon - i - ca, Mon - i - ca, dance the waltz.
Mo - ni - ca, Mo - ni - ca, valse en - core,   Mo - ni - ca, Mo - ni - ca, valse en - core.

a tempo

Fol - low   me,   moon   and   sun,   Fol - low me,   fol - low, fol - low
Sui - vez - moi,   un(e)   deux trois,   sui - vez - moi,   sui - vez - moi,   so -

me, fol - low me,   fol - low, fol - low   me.
leil_ et   lune,_   et vo - lons   aux cieux.

(Toby seizes Monica abruptly by the arm. She turns and
looks at him in complete
astonishment.)

*(Toby saisit brusquement
le bras de Monica. Elle
se retourne et le regarde,
stupéfaite.)*   What   is the mat-ter, To-by?   What is it you want to tell me?
   Qu'est-c(e) qui te prend, To-by?   Qu'est-ce que tu veux me dire?_

p (senza misura)

66

41701

68

poco rit.

a tempo

M.

and still I love you and al - ways loved you with all my breath, with all my blood.
pour - tant je t'aime et je t'ai ai - mée___ de tout mon souffle, tou - te mon âme.___

rit.

a tempo

poco animando

M.

I love your laugh - ter, I love your hair, I love your deep and noc - tur - nal eyes.
J'ai - me ton rire,___ j'ai - me tes yeux, J'ai - me tes yeux aux re - gards de nuit,

poco animando

M.

I love your soft hands, so white and winged, I love the slen - der branch of your throat.
tes mains si blanches aux dou-ceurs d'ailes, Et le char-mant des - sin de tes veines.

rall.

più f

cresc.

f

rall.

(She stands up before him)
(Elle revient devant lui)

(She runs
behind Toby)
*(Elle passe
derrière Toby)*

a tempo

M.

⑥ To - by, don't speak to me like that! You make my head___ swim.
To - by, ne par - le pas ain - si,___ ma tê - te cha - vi - re.

pp subito

41701

poco riten., poi subito animando

Mon - i - ca, Mon - i - ca, fold me in your sat - in gown. Mon - i - ca, Mon - i - ca, give me your
Mo - ni - ca, rou - le-moi dans ta ro-be de sa - tin. Mo - ni - ca, don - ne moi — tes

mouth, Mon - i - ca, Mon - i - ca, fall in my arms.
levres, Mo - ni - ca, Mo - ni - ca, viens dans mes bras.

a tempo, ma più mosso

allarg. molto

(Toby suddenly hides
his face in his arms.)
*(Tout a coup, Toby cache
son visage dans ses bras.)*

(Monica stares at him,
completely bewildered.)
*(Monica le regarde,
abasourdie.)*

Why, To - by! You're not cry - ing, are you?
Mais, To - by! Mais ne pleu - re donc pas?

a tempo *long pause*

(She caresses his head. Then lifting his
tear-stained face, looks into his eyes)
*(Elle lui caresse la tête; et soulevant son
visage en pleurs, le regarde dans les yeux)*

(with great tenderness)
(avec une grande tendresse)

To - by, I want you to know
To - by, tu dois le sa - voir

⑦

ppp teneramente

M.

that you have _____ the most beau-ti-ful voice _____ in the world! _____
tu pos - sèdes _____ la plus bel - le voix _____ du monde! _____

pp   *mf*   *pp*   *ppp*

(Door slams. Baba is heard dragging herself up the stairs. Monica runs out, into her room.
Toby crouches in the corner)
*(Bruit de porte; on entend le pas de Baba montant lourdement l'escalier. Monica s'enfuit dans
sa chambre. Toby va se tapir dans un coin)*

Allegro molto moderato ♩.= 96

ff   *pp*

(Baba appears,
(Baba paraît,

dark, dishevelled, a bottle in her hand)
sombre, échevelée, une bouteille à la main)

Baba

Baba

Where is Mon-i - ca?
Où est Mo - ni-ca?

⑧

f   *f* *stent.*   *a piacere*   *p*

(Toby points to the door at the right. Baba takes off her large shawl and sits meditatively
(Toby montre la porte de droite. Baba retire son grand châle et va s'asseoir à la table.

at the table)
Elle demeure pensive)

Adagio ♩ = 44

Allegro moderato ♩ = 96

(with strained affection)
(avec une feinte tendresse)

To - by,   what are you do - ing?
To - by,   que fais - tu donc là-bas?

Come here, To - by.
Ap - pro - che - toi.

(Toby begins to crawl toward her, but very
hesitatingly, with apparent misgivings)
*(Toby, avec beaucoup d'hésitation, se met
à glisser vers elle, visiblement effrayé)*

I want to talk to you.   Come,   come near   me.
Par-lons un peu, nous deux.   Viens,   plus près de moi.

(senza misura)

Poco più
mosso ♩. = 63

intenso

where would you be now? I found you, a lit-tle starv-ing
où se-rais-tu, sans moi? Je t'ai vu, pe-tit tzigane af - fa-

gip-sy, roam-ing the streets of Bu-da-pest with-out a tongue to speak your
mé er-rant dans les rues de Bu-da-pest sans voix pour dire qu'il a - vait

poco rit.

Poco meno mosso ♪ = 56

hun - ger. If I had-n't tak-en you with me,
faim? Si je ne t'a-vais pas pris a - vec moi,

mf

poco rit.

Poco più mosso di prima
quasi andante ♩. = 58

who would have cared for you, poor lit - tle half-wit? And now,
qui au-rait pris soin de toi, pe-tit de-meu - ré? Maint(e)-nant, é -

⑩

p a tempo

Were you the one who touched my throat?
si c'est toi qui m'as prise à la gorge?

You know, at the se-ance a few days a-go...
Pendant la sé-ance, tu sais, il y a quelques jours...

Don't be a-
N'aie donc pas

fraid of tell-ing me.
peur de l'a-vou-er.

I won't pun - - ish you.
Je ne te pu - ni-rai pas.

rall.

Poco meno

I just want to know,
Je veux ê - tre fix - ée,—

that is all.
sim-ple - ment.

see?
sible?
But you know you saw it! I can
Mais toi, tu sais, tu l'as vu! Je puis

read it in your eyes!
li - re dans tes yeux!
Come on, say yes, or
Al - lons, dis oui, ou

(Toby tries to run away; she
Toby essaie de fuir, elle le

no!
non!
Stop star - ing at me!
Cesse___ de me bra - ver!
Don't go a -
Ne t'en vas

grabs him by his shirt and tears it off his back)
saisit par sa chemise qu'elle lui arrache)

Andante calmo ♩. = 69

way!
pas!
You see,
Tu vois,
you're mak - ing me
voi - là que tu me

Allegro ♩.= 96
liberamente, senza battuta *(declamato*)*
(with mounting excitement)
(de plus en plus agitée)

Baba: an - gry a-gain! You love Mon - i - ca, don't you?
fâches, de nou-veau! Tu ai - mes Mo-ni - ca, n'est-c(e) pas?

Baba: How would you like to mar-ry her? Yes, you could, you could.
Que di - rais-tu de l'é - pou-ser? La chose est fai - sable.

Baba: But first you must tell me, did you have
Mais il faut que je sa - che si tu é-

---

*Whenever "declamato" appears in this score, the rhythm and pitch indicated are to be regarded as only approximate.

**Chaque fois que se présente l'indication "declamato" la chanteuse évitera de suivre exactement le rythme. Elle ne rendra aussi qu'approximativement la tessiture de la partie vocale.*

Baba: You're try-ing to fright-en me. I'll show you, damn lit-tle gip-
Tu vou-drais me fai-re peur, tu a-voue-ras, vi-lain tzi-

(She goes to the cupboard and brings out a long whip. Toby runs away from her in terror)
(Elle va vers l'armoire et en retire un long fouet. Terrorisé, Toby se détourne)

Baba: sy, I'll make you talk!
gane, tu a-voue-ras!

Baba: I'll make you talk! You can-not get a-way
Je sau-rai tout! Tu ne pour-ras pas m'é-chap-

(She chases him around the table.)
(Elle le poursuit autour de la table.)

from me! / I'll make you spit out blood,
per! / Même si tu dois cra-cher

(Toby trips and falls near the couch)
(Toby trébuche et tombe près du canapé)

I will. / I'll make you spit out blood!
ton sang. / Je sau-rai te faire a-vou-er!

Meno mosso

(She whips him)
(Elle le fouette)

So you won't an-swer, eh!
Veux-tu ré-pon-dre, ah!

(She whips him)
(Elle le fouette encore)

So you won't an-swer, eh!
Veux-tu ré-pon-dre, ah!

fff pesante

(whips him)
(fouet)

So you won't an-swer, eh!
Veux-tu ré-pon-dre, ah!

(whips him)
(fouet)

So you won't an-swer, eh!
Veux tu ré-pon-dre, ah!

fff

84

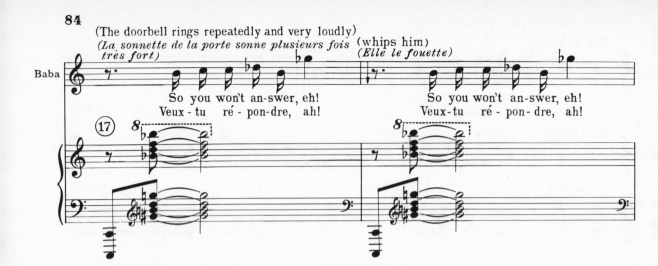

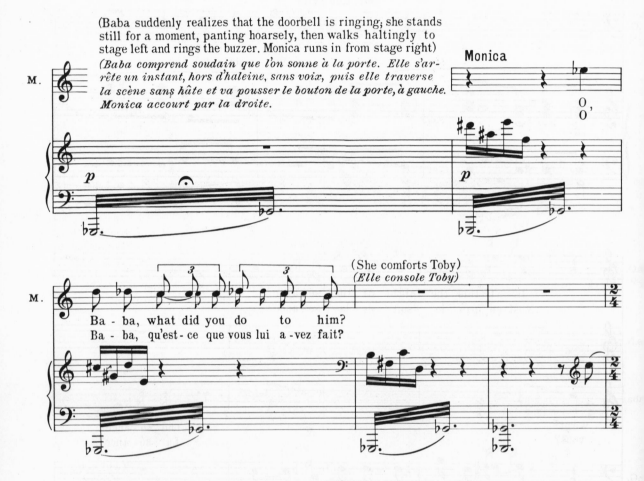

(Mr. and Mrs. Gobineau and Mrs. Nolan come up the stairs. They stop rather surprised on the landing)
(*M. et Mme. Gobineau, avec Mme. Nolan arrivent au haut de l'escalier et s'arrêtent, assez surpris, sur le palier*)

Andante ma un poco più mosso del primo atto ♩ = 60

88

41701

92

41701

won't let us down! / What would we do with-out your gui-dance?
cher main-te-nant! / Qu'est-ce que nous fe-rions sans votre ai-de?

won't let us down! / What would we do with-out your gui-dance?
cher main-te-nant! / Qu'est-ce que nous fe-rions sans votre ai-de?

You must be-lieve me!
Il faut me croire!

won't let us down! / What would we do with-out your gui-dance?
cher main-te-nant! / Qu'est-ce que nous fe-rions sans votre ai-de?

(The three clients suddenly stand expressionless like automatons.)
(Tout a coup, les clients se figent, impassibles, comme des automates.)

Please let us have our se-ance, Ma-dame Flo-ra! / Just let us hear it once
Don-nez-nous no-tre sé-an-ce, Ma-da-me! / Rien qu'u-ne fois, u-ne

Please let us have our se-ance, Ma-dame Flo-ra! / Just let us hear it once
Don-nez-nous no-tre sé-an-ce, Ma-da-me! / Rien qu'u-ne fois, u-ne

(declaimed at a high pitch, as before)
(declamé, très haut, comme avant)

It is foolish of you!
Vous êtes vraiment fous!

Please let us have our se-ance, Ma-dame Flo-ra! / Just let us hear it once
Don-nez-nous no-tre sé-an-ce, Ma-da-me! / Rien qu'u-ne fois, u-ne

pp senza affrettare

100

41701

(Monica sees the pup-
pets lying on the floor.
She picks them up.)
*(Monica voit les marion-
nettes étendues à terre
et les ramasse.)*

Allegretto moderato

Baba

Don't stand there like a fool!
Ne fais pas tant d'histoires!

Go in-to your room!
Vas dans ta chambre,

(Monica goes into her room, banging the door.
Baba is left alone on stage)
*(Monica rentre dans sa chambre en faisant
claquer la porte. Baba reste seule sur la scène)*

Baba

Leave him a-lone. He'll take care of him-self.
n'y pen-se plus. Il sau-ra s'ar-ran-ger.

più mosso ♩.= 96

Voice

Moth-er, moth-er, are you there?
Mè - re, mè - re, est - ce toi?

(She stands stock-still
and terror-stricken.)
(Elle écoute, immobile
et terrifiée.)

Who's there? Is it you, Monica?
Qui est là? C'est toi, Monica?

(She abruptly moves toward the
bedroom. After listening at the
door, she quickly locks it, then leans
against it with a sigh of relief.)
(Elle se dirige brusquement vers
la chambre de Monica. Elle écoute
à la porte, la ferme à clef, et s'y ap-
puie avec un soupir de soulage-
ment.)

Adagio

Allegro ♩. = 112

㉙

ppp

pp

(She begins to walk toward the table.)
(Elle se dirige vers la table.)

ff

(long
silence)
(un long
silence)

Voice

Moth - er, moth - er, are you there? Moth - er, moth - er, are you there?
Mè - re, mè - re, est - ce toi? Mè - re, mè - re, est - ce toi?

(At the sound of the voice, she stands frozen.)
(Au son de la voix, elle se fige, pétrifiée.)

(interrupting (shouted)
the voice (crié)
with a cry)
(D'un cri, elle
fait taire la   Stop it!
voix.)   Silence!

Adagio

ppp

(She goes to the cupboard and pours herself several drinks, then brings the bottle and glass to the table. She sits down)
(Elle prend une bouteille dans le buffet et se verse un plein verre de liqueur. Elle boit et va s'asseoir à la table)

Baba: dead! The dead... the dead...
morts, Les morts... les morts...

Andante molto maestoso ♩ = 52

Baba: the dead nev-er come back. They sink down in the
les morts ne re-vien-nent pas. Ils s'a-bîment dans la pous-

③③ *fff*

accelerando molto

Baba: dust with no eyes to dream and no si-lence to
sière, sans yeux pour rê-ver sans lèv-res pour men-

mf cresc.

*No breath should be taken between the last note and the spoken phrase.

On ne doit pas respirer entre la dernière note musicale et la phrase parlée.

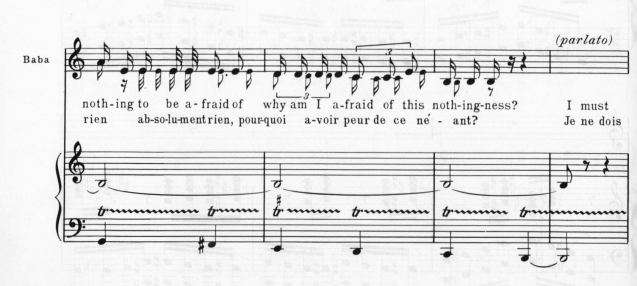

114

41701

(She falls asleep)
(*Elle s'endort*)

(Toby comes up the stairwell.)
(*Toby paraît sur le palier.*)

(Cautiously, he walks tiptoe to Monica's door)
(*Avec précaution, sur la pointe des pieds, il s'approche de la porte de Monica*)

Andante con moto ♪ = 92

Allegretto ♩. = 66

(He finds the door locked)
(Il trouve la porte fermée à clef)

(He scratches softly on the door)
(Il gratte doucement à la porte)

(Baba stirs in her sleep, knocking the bottle down. Toby runs behind the couch, then very slowly creeps out again)
(Baba s'agite dans son sommeil et fait tomber la bouteille. Toby court se cacher derrière le divan, puis, très lentement, il se montre de nouveau)

(Toby again tries the door)
(Toby essaie encore d'ouvrir la porte)

(He knocks at it,
whimpering softly
like an animal.)
*(Il frappe à la porte,
geignant doucement
comme un animal.)*

(Receiving no answer, Toby runs to the trunk and begins to rummage among the silks in search of his tambourine.)
(Ne recevant aucune réponse, Toby court jusqu'au coffre et se met à fouiller parmi les soieries, à la recherche de son tambourin.)

(The trunk lid falls sharply)
(Le couvercle du coffre tombe brusquement)

(Baba wakes up with a start. Toby hides behind the curtain of the puppet theater)
(Baba se réveille en sursaut. Toby se cache derrière le rideau du théâtre de marionnettes)

Who's there? Qui est là?

40 Allegro agitato ♩=144

(The curtain moves. Baba screams
and fires at it several times.)

*(Le rideau s'agite. Baba hurle et
tire à plusieurs reprises dans sa
direction.)*

An - swer me! An - swer me! I'll shoot! I'll shoot!
Ré - ponds moi! Ré - ponds moi! Je vais ti - rer!

(Suddenly Toby's hand appears
above the curtain, as if to ward
off the bullets. Then the fin-
gers slowly clench and the hand
disappears.)

*(Soudain, la main de Toby ap-
paraît au-dessus du rideau,
comme pour repousser les
balles. Puis les doigts se cris-
pent et la main disparaît.)*

(The curtain is now clutched tightly from inside. A spot
of blood gradually appears and runs the length of the
white cloth.)

*(Le rideau est maintenant empoigné fortement de l'intér-
ieur. Une tache de sang apparaît et s'allonge en descendant
jusqu'au bas du rideau.)*

Molto lento ♩ = 84

♩ = 72

I've killed the ghost!
J'ai tu-é l'es-prit!

Baba: I've killed the ghost! / J'ai tu - é l'es-prit!

(Both of Toby's hands are now seen clutching at the curtain. The rod breaks under his weight, and, wrapped in the curtain, he falls headlong into the room.)

(On voit maintenant les mains de Toby étreignant le rideau. La tringle se brise sous son poids; enroulé dans le rideau, il s'écroule, la tête la première.)

Poco più mosso (in 2)

(Monica pounds at the door from within)

(Monica, enfermée, frappe la porte à coups répetés)

Baba: I've killed the ghost! / J'ai tu - é l'es-prit!

p subito

(Baba slowly unlocks the door. Monica rushes in.)

(Baba ouvre lentement le porte. Monica se précipite.)

Monica
(parlato)

Baba! Baba! Let me in! Let me in! / Baba! Baba! Ouvrez - moi! Ouvrez - moi!

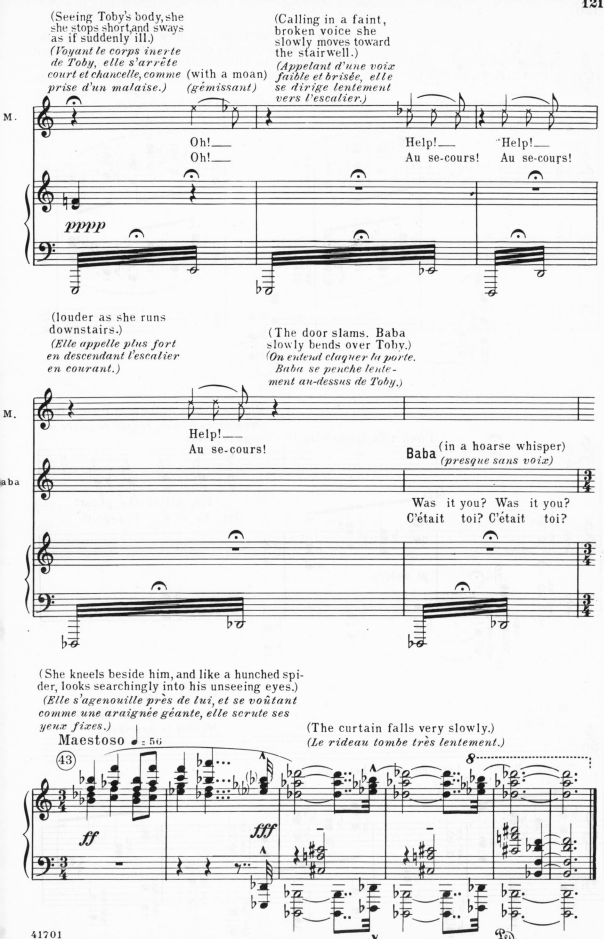